CONTENTS

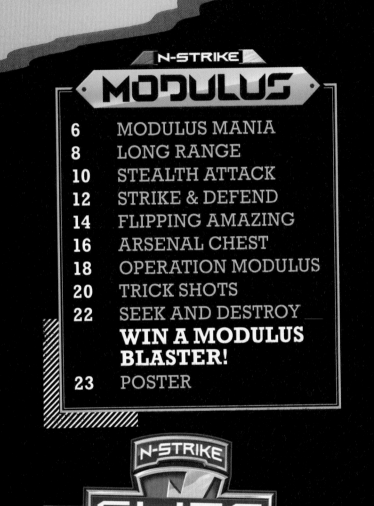

IT'S NERF OR NOTHIN'!

Published 2015. Pedigree Books Limited, Beech Hill House,
Walnut Gardens, Exeter, Devon EX4 4DH.
www.pedigreebooks.com – books@pedigreegroup.co.uk
The Pedigree trademark, email and website addresses, are the sole and exclusive
properties of Pedigree Group Limited, used under licence in this publication.

MODULUS MANIA!

THIS BLASTER CAN DO IT ALL...

4

7

THE LOW-DOWN:

The Modulus ECS-10 blaster comes with 6 different accessories allowing you to modify it up to 30 different blaster combinations. It has a targeting scope, drop grip and dual-rail barrel as well as a 10-dart banana clip and darts. It's cool white design and "build your own" feature makes it the most-awesome blaster for miles.

6

KNOWS

Including all the upgrade kits, the Modulus has over 1000 configuration options!

1000+

CHECK THIS OUT!

NERF KNOWS

There are four different upgrade kits allowing up to 1000 different combinations! Turn the page to get up to speed on the Long Range, Stealth Ops, Strike & Defend and Flip Clip upgrade kits!

LABEL IT!

Can you identify all the different parts of the Modulus from 1 to 6? We're not going to make it easy for you, you'll have to unscramble the letters first.

1: UDLE ARLI ABRERL

2: TRADS

3: OOMTRIDZE LBTASRE

4: GTRAEGTIN COSPE

5: RDPO RGPI

6: ABNNAA RGIP

7: GRESOAT KOTSC

3

1

CHECK THIS OUT!

SCAN ME

5

2

IN TRAINING

When choosing how to adapt your Modulus – or even which blaster to use – always think about your mission, first. Who's on the other side? What's your objective? Then go from there...

LONG RANGE   **STEALTH ATTACK**   **STRIKE & DEFEND**   **FLIP CLIP**

MODULUS
N-STRIKE

LONG RANGE

ADAPT YOUR BLASTER TO TAKE ON
FAR AWAY TARGETS WITH EASE.

DISTANCE SCOPE

FOLDING BIPOD

THE LOW-DOWN:

This full battle kit includes a distance
scope for precision targeting, a folding
bipod to steady your long shots, and a
long barrel to increase your distance
accuracy. When you upgrade the ECS-
10 blaster, you're taking your game
to the next level! Tackle targets while
keeping your position safe and stealth.

IN TRAINING

To get the best distance,
always hold your blaster
at a 45 degree angle and
make a note of which
way the wind is blowing.

EYE ON THE PRIZE!

Once you have your long range modifications in place, follow these top tips for the ultimate target training.

1. Find somewhere with a lot of space. Outside is best.

2. Find a spot to blast from, then copy or cut out the targets from this page. Mark out targets at different distances. Use sticky tape or drawing pins to attach them.

3. Start by trying to hit the targets closest to you, then hit the targets further away. Use your long range modifications to hit the targets first time.

STEALTH ATTACK

WANT TO BE A SNIPER? KEEP YOUR OPERATION FIRMLY UNDERCOVER.

RED DOT SIGHT

MODULUS

NERF

PIVOT GRIP

THE LOW-DOWN:

When you need accuracy and secrecy on a covert operation, the Stealth Ops Kit is there. The kit includes a Red Dot Sight and a Proximity Barrel for precision targeting and a Pivot Grip for a steadier shot. Combine with your long range options for the ultimate stealth blaster!

IN TRAINING

When you're undercover, you need to think about more than just your blaster. Plan your operation fatigues well: make sure you don't wear anything too bright and wear soft-soled shoes so no one hears you coming!

COVERT OPERATIONS

When heading up a stealth mission, you'll need to do everything you can to keep your position and your plans under wraps. Figure out what the message says, then use the code to send messages to your friends!

@*2O•   HK*:   F$*=+

PRACTICE YOUR CODE HERE...

CODE

A$	B@	CS
DF	E:	F>
G•	H<	I2
JQ	K4	L7
MH	NO	OK
P6	Q#	R*
S+	T=	U9
VB	WL	Y£
Y?	Z/	

STRIKE AND DEFEND

BLAST SHIELD

MINI BLASTER

IN TRAINING

Never shoot darts at an opponent's face, even in the heat of battle!

THE LOW-DOWN:

The Strike & Defend kit comes with an amazing shield and mini blaster. The shield defends you from darts, while the blaster gives you one extra shot for when you're out of darts. The blaster can be clipped to the back of your modulus, then pulled out quickly for emergency situations.

TOP TIPS

Check out our three best defence and attack techniques before unleashing your skills onto the battlefield!

STRIKE!

1. Keep your darts close by for quick re-loading! Use a flip clip to give you extra time!

2. Choose your moment! Watch what your opponents are doing and strike when you see a weakness in their formation.

3. Be confident! When you have made the decision to attack, stay with it! If you're unsure, your enemies will pick up on it.

DEFEND!

1. Keep your eyes open! Remember, enemies can be lurking almost anywhere.

2. Keep quiet! If your opponents can hear you, they'll be able to fire at you!

3. Keep your shield on your blaster. Better safe than sorry!

Over to you! Use this space to write down your best strike and defence tactics.

STRIKE!

DEFEND!

NERF

N-STRIKE MODULUS

FLIPPING AMAZING

TOO BUSY TO RELOAD? THANK GOODNESS FOR THE FLIP CLIP!

FLIP CLIP

THE LOW-DOWN:

The Modulus Flip Clip holds two rounds of 12 darts, giving you a 24 dart capacity with in-play dart rotation. All you need to do is pull out your magazine when done, flip it over and slot in the other side. Just amazing!

● ● ○ ○ ○

IN TRAINING

Make sure your darts are at their optimum performance levels by keeping them somewhere dry and making sure they don't get crushed or mis-shapen.

14

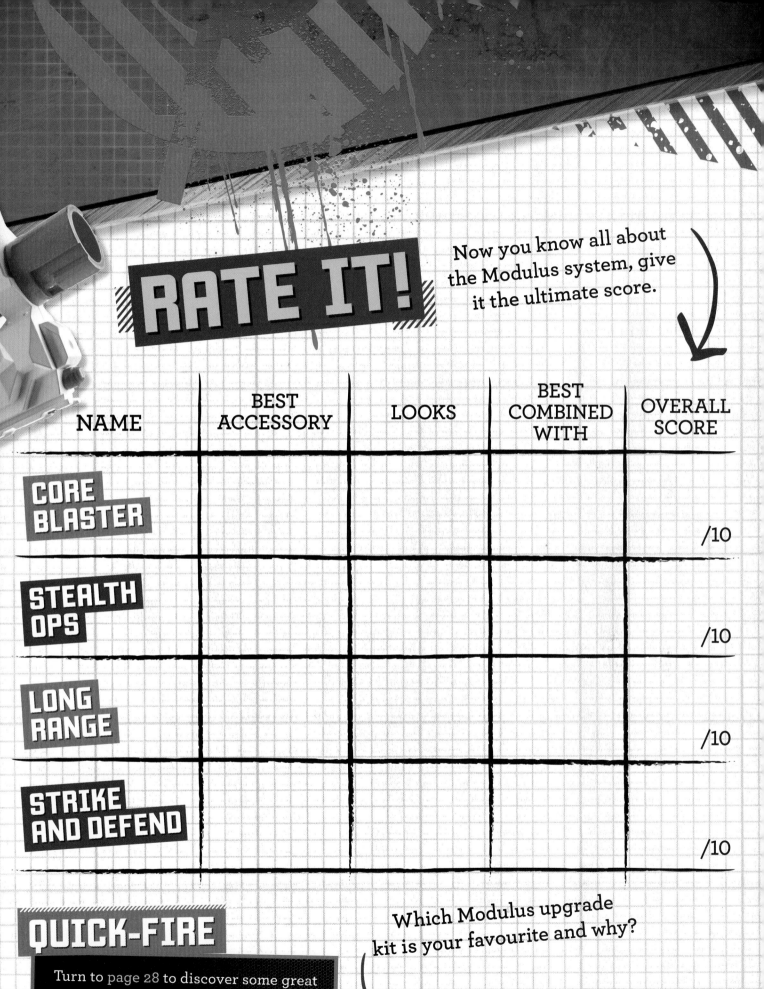

RATE IT!

Now you know all about the Modulus system, give it the ultimate score.

NAME	BEST ACCESSORY	LOOKS	BEST COMBINED WITH	OVERALL SCORE
CORE BLASTER				/10
STEALTH OPS				/10
LONG RANGE				/10
STRIKE AND DEFEND				/10

QUICK-FIRE

Which Modulus upgrade kit is your favourite and why?

Turn to page 28 to discover some great target practice ideas. Now get the stopclock out! Are you as quick as your friends? Time each event and keep a record to see who the winner is.

ARSENAL CHEST

Your Modulus Blaster could have up to 15 different components. Create this cool chest to keep them in order and close at hand!

YOU WILL NEED

Plain lidded box (around 40.5 x 32 x 25cm)

Scissors or a craft knife

Glue

Cereal box

Three pieces of elastic – 9cm long

Shoe box

Paint

STEP 1

Take your cereal box and tape up the lid. Place the box on its side and use scissors or a craft knife to take off one of the sides. You should now have a box with an opening on one of the thin sides. Add glue to the front or back of the cereal packet and glue it to the inside of your lidded box at one of the shorter ends. Make sure the hole you have made is at the top as this will be your flip clip and darts storage.

Using your scissors or a craft knife, make three sets of two holes along one of the long sides of your box. Each pair of holes should be 5cm apart.

5 cms

Now take a piece of elastic and make a knot on one end. Thread the other end through one of the holes going from the outside in. Thread the other end through the next hole and tie a knot so that the elastic lies flat against the side of the box. Do the same with the two other sets of holes to create three loops. These loops can hold your pivot grip, proximity barrel and distance scope.

STEP 3

Remove the lid of your shoe box and glue the bottom to the inside of your box. Place it on the opposite side to your cereal box to leave a small amount of room in the middle, then replace the lid. The shoe box can be used for smaller modifications.

STEP 4

Now you have the structure of your chest, it's time to make it look the part! Paint your chest white inside and out to give it uniformity. Don't forget the lid! Add strips of orange and lime green to match your blaster – you could even add your initials to let everyone know this is your arsenal!

STEP 5

Once the paint is dry, add your Blaster and upgrades. Your core Modulus Blaster should fit in the gap between your Flip Clip and darts holder and your inner box.

NERF

OPERATION MODULUS

Play this cool game with friends using your Modulus (or any other) blaster.

YOU WILL NEED

Paper
Sticky tape or drawing pin
Dice

HOW TO PLAY

Copy or cut out the playing pieces and place them on the start square.

Copy the wheel, left, onto a piece of A4 paper and pin or stick it to a wall.

Standing at least three metres away from the wheel, use your blaster to hit a number then move that number along the board.

When you land on a Long Range, Strike & Defend or Stealth Ops square you must complete a mission before moving on to the next square.

PLAYING PIECES

NUMBER WHEEL

1 START!

2 →

3 STEALTH OPS
The rest of the players must close their eyes and count to 10 while you hide somewhere in the room. If they can't spot you without leaving their seats – move forward three spaces.

4 ↓

8 ↓

7 STRIKE & DEFEND
The rest of the players must stand at least three metres away from you and each fire a single dart. If you can knock the darts out of the air before they hit you – move forward three spaces.

6 ←

5 Run out of darts!
GO BACK ONE SPACE.

9 Nice shot!
MOVE FORWARD ONE SPACE

10 →

11 LONG RANGE
Stand as far away from the door of the room you are playing in. You have one chance to fire a dart through the door, if you do – move forward three spaces.

12 ↓

16 ↓

15 STEALTH OPS
If you can name the exact number of darts the rest of the players have loaded into their blasters right now – move forward three spaces.

14 ←

13 No! Your blaster is jammed!
MOVE BACK ONE SPACE.

17 Re-loaded in record time!
MOVE FORWARD ONE SPACE

18 →

19 STRIKE & DEFEND
Use the door of the room you are playing in as a shield. If you can hit your fellow players without getting hit yourself – move forward three spaces.

20 ↓

24 ↓

23 LONG RANGE
Stand as far away from a window in the room you are playing in. You have one chance to fire a dart through the open window, if you do – move forward three spaces.

22 ←

21 Your line of vision is blocked.
MOVE BACK ONE SPACE

25 It's nearly mission complete!
MOVE FORWARD ONE SPACE

26 →

27 You let your guard down too early!
MISS A TURN

28 YOU WIN!

19

TRICK SHOT

USE ALL FOUR OF YOUR UPGRADE KITS TO GET A CLEAN SWEEP OF TRICKSHOTS!

LONG DISTANCE RELATIONSHIP

Get a friend to take two balls (a football and a tennis ball are ideal) and walk at least 10 metres away. Ask your friend to keep the balls at their side until you shout 'Go!' It's up to your friend to decide how he holds up the balls, and it's up to you to blast them as quickly as you can!

IN TRAINING

Trickshots look cool for a reason – they've usually taken the trick-shotter hours to perfect! Don't give up if you don't get your chosen shot right first time, stick at it – it'll be worth it!

MAKE IT COUNT!

When you've only got one shot left, you've got to make it count. Place two paper cups on top of each other, as below. Place an empty raisin box or small container on top. Use your last shot in the Stock Shot of your Strike & Defend kit to knock the top paper cup out of the way, leaving the raisin box to fall into the bottom cup.

● ● ● ● ○

ON TARGET

Use your Stealth Ops kit to land your dart in exactly the right place. Use an empty drinks bottle with the lid off and lie it on its side on top of a stack of books. Find a position with a similar height (behind a chair or table) and see if you can fire a single dart into the bottle.

● ● ● ● ○

NERF N-STRIKE MODULUS

SEEK & DESTROY

WIN A MODULUS BLASTER

20 TO WIN!

Now you know everything there is to know about the awesome Modulus Blaster, see if you can seek out the hidden words in this grid Find them all, send in your completed grid and be in with the chance to **WIN ONE OF 20 MODULUS ECS-10 BLASTERS!**

FIND

- BLASTER
- CLIP
- COMBINATION
- DARTS
- DEFEND
- STRIKE
- FLIP
- LONG
- MODULUS
- OPERATION
- OPS
- RANGE
- STEALTH
- TARGET
- UPGRADE

N	K	S	A	F	E	L	R	J	N	Z	G	E	E	P
G	O	B	T	G	L	E	F	L	O	R	B	Q	U	L
E	E	I	N	E	T	I	Y	O	I	P	Y	C	H	B
M	U	A	T	S	A	I	P	N	T	H	W	R	Y	F
J	R	W	A	A	M	L	H	G	A	J	L	A	E	H
R	Z	L	M	T	N	F	T	T	R	D	U	W	S	O
G	B	Q	Y	U	G	I	K	H	E	E	H	W	T	A
M	O	D	U	L	U	S	B	O	P	G	M	H	R	R
N	M	F	J	E	D	Q	P	M	O	T	R	B	A	K
C	L	I	P	E	D	S	N	Y	O	M	A	A	D	Z
Q	J	U	F	E	K	I	R	T	S	C	Q	T	T	B
A	K	E	Q	E	L	D	R	P	W	S	I	Q	E	C
X	N	C	G	P	K	Z	T	R	K	E	Q	W	Q	L
D	D	R	K	T	Z	H	U	P	G	R	A	D	E	Z
W	F	Q	W	Z	R	E	T	Y	E	T	Y	V	H	I

Check out the competition details plus terms and conditions on page 60.

CRUISING WITH THE CROSSBOLT

GET PREPPED FOR FLYING FIREPOWER WITH THE AMAZING CROSSBOLT!

⚠ ATTENTION:
Ne pas viser les yeux ni le visage.
POUR ÉVITER TOUTE BLESSURE:
n'utiliser que les fléchettes conçues pour ce produit. Ne pas modifier les fléchettes ni le lance-fléchettes.

⚠ PRECAUCIÓN:
No apuntes a los ojos ni a la cara. **PARA EVITAR LESIONES:**
Utiliza sólo los dardos diseñados para este producto. No modifiques los dardos ni la lanzadardos.

THE LOW-DOWN:

Make your mission count with this high-capacity crossbow. The Nerf N-Strike Elite CrossBolt blaster comes with a 12-dart orange clip that, once loaded, means you're ready for exciting clip-fed crossbow action. Unleash a barrage of darts, then reload the clip and let the darts fly again! Give the competition a dozen reasons to run and hide when you go into battle...

TRIGGER

12 DART CLIP

NERF

NERF KNOWS

The bright colours on this blaster were designed for enhanced visibility outdoors!

IN TRAINING

Keep an extra clip of darts somewhere easy to pull out. Your back pocket is the perfect place!

VISION VERIFICATION

BOW PRIMER

CROSSBOW

To use a CrossBolt you need eagle-eyed vision. Practice your skills by finding 6 differences in the images below.

INTO THE WOODS

HOW TO PLAY

First thing you need to do is choose whether you are going to play indoors or outdoors.

PLAY THIS GAME INDOORS OR OUTSIDE.

IT'S ALL ABOUT TIMING AND SKILL!

OUTDOORS

Pick a spot with plenty of trees. Decide on a start point and finish point (they should be a good distance away from each other). One player is chosen to be the hunter and takes the CrossBolt (or any blaster you want to play with) then turns around and counts to 30 while the rest of the players spread out, choosing hiding spots individually.

The game begins once the hunter reaches 30 and turns back around. The aim of the game is for players to join up and move from hiding place to hiding place without being blasted by the hunter.

INDOORS

Follow the same rules as above, but use your house and furniture as hiding places.

5 **5** **10**

10

15

15

SCORING

Copy or cut out these six points medallions from this page. The hiders each take a medallion and pin it to their clothes. When all the players have either been blasted or have made it to the finish point, it's time to add up the points. Blasted players' points go to the hunter, while the players who made it to the end add their points together. Whoever has the most points is the winner!

TARGET PRACTICE

Keep your aim sharp with these cool target ideas.

CUP PYRAMID

You'll need 10 paper or plastic cups for this one. Don't use glass or anything that could break, (unless you really want to get into trouble)! Build your cups into a pyramid, as shown above. Stand 10 paces away from your pyramid and fire. See how many darts it takes you to knock the pyramid down, then try to beat it. Move further away from the pyramid to make it even harder.

BALLOON BREAK

Balloons make a tricky target as they move about, even indoors! Use string to tie your balloons to various places (trees are great if you are outside, cupboards and door handles work well for indoors.) Get 5 points for hitting the balloon, 10 points for popping it!

SIZE IT UP

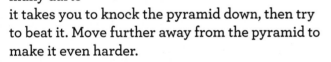

Collect objects in different shapes and sizes that won't break easily such as action figures, fruit and veg, tennis ball, books, stuffed toys, empty packets (raid the recycling bin). Line them up on a bench or table top. Award more points for hitting the smaller objects, and less points for hitting the bigger objects.

KEEP ON MOVING!

Ask a friend to throw paper plates up into the air like a vertical Frisbee. Try to hit the plates with your blaster. The coolest thing about this training exercise is that, once you've picked up your plates, you should be able to see where you hit and improve your aim next time!

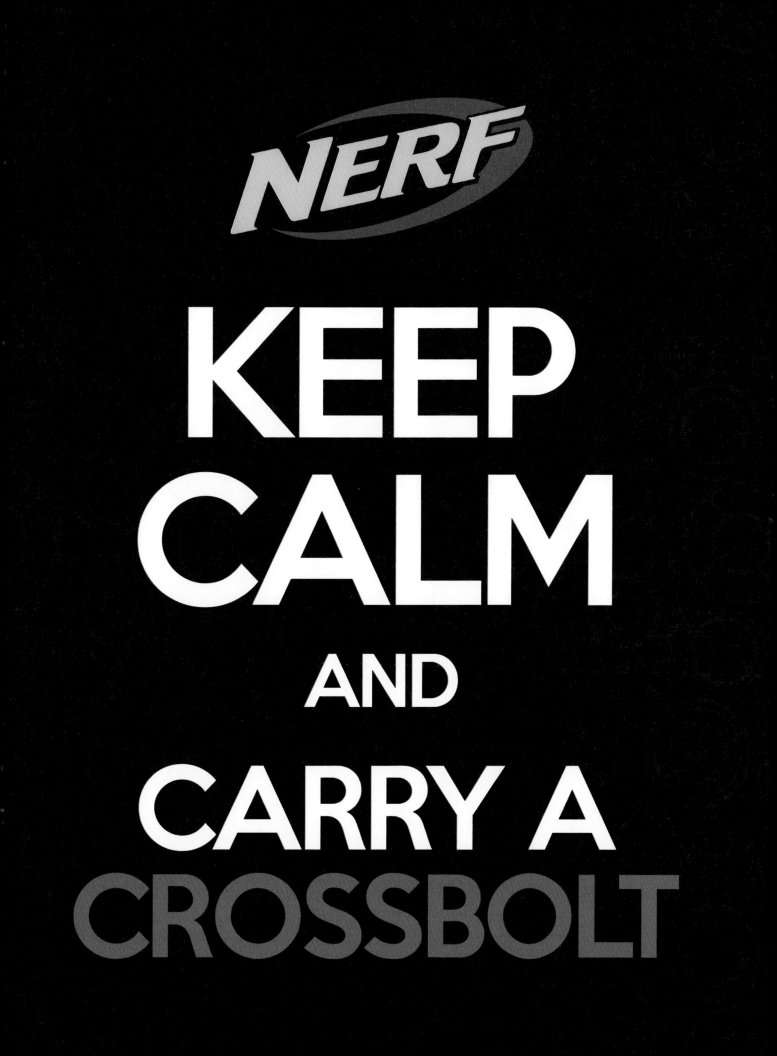

DISCOVER YOUR PERFECT BLASTER

Answer the questions to discover which blaster is your ideal match!

QUESTION 1

The most important thing about a blaster is...

A	It's power
B	It's speed
C	It's accuracy
D	It's adaptability

QUESTION 2

On a mission, you...

A	Are first in line. You love the action!
B	Blast first, ask questions later
C	Take your time and make every shot count
D	Plan, plan, plan

QUESTION 3

What size blaster do you like?

A	The bigger the better!
B	Big, with loads of darts
C	Medium
D	I'd like a blaster that can change to suit me!

QUESTION 4

Pick a colour

A	Red
B	Green
C	Blue
D	White

QUESTION 5

Pick the best job

A	Demolition man
B	Athlete
C	Body guard
D	Secret agent

QUESTION 6

Which one describes you best?

A	Loud and powerful
B	Quick and fun
C	Calm under pressure
D	Clever and confident

ROTOFURY

MEGA NERF

NERF

12-16
ROTOFURY

When you're on a mission, you want everyone to know you mean business. With the Rotofury, you'll have power on your side. The 10-dart rotating drum and large darts reach up to 21 meters, so you're sure to get a maximum impact!

17-21
DOOMINATOR

You know when you're under attack (especially by Zombies) the best way to handle them is with as many darts as possible. With 24 darts in one loading – the Doominator will be your best friend on any mission.

22-25
CROSSBOLT

You make each dart count and accuracy is your middle name (not really, that would be weird). The CrossBolt gives you the time and power to hit targets with pinpoint precision – even from long distances! Your stealth missions will always run to plan with this blaster.

27-30
MODULUS

You like to be prepared before each mission. Super prepared. And that's why the Modulus Blaster is your perfect match. With over 1000 different combinations, you can adapt your blaster for any situation.

NERF

ZOMBIE STRIKE

FULL-ON FLIPFURY

FLIPFURY

NERF

LOWDOWN

Unleash a sweeping zombie-blasting defence with this hardcore Zombie Strike Blaster! The blaster's double flipping drums hold six darts each and let you fire up to 12 darts without reloading. Perfect for when a fleet of the undead are at your feet!

In a zombie apocalypse, you're going to need speed and power. Luckily, the Flipfury has both!

WATCH OUT!

Can you spot 12 zombies to hit with your blaster hidden around these two pages?

NERF KNOWS

It only takes one flick of the trigger to change barrels and double your firepower!

THE DOOMINATOR

12 darts not enough? Try 24! The Doominator spells trouble for zombies - no matter how fast they're coming or how big the pack.

Doominator

NERF

ZOMBIE STRIKE® Doominator

NERF

CUSTOM MADE

If you could customise your blaster with any colours, what would it look like? Well, now you've got the chance!

NERF KNOWS

You can move the slide grip to three different positions. You can have it underneath, or on the side to the left or right – depending on whether you are left or right handed.

LOWDOWN

The Doominator rains down 24 darts at high speed thanks to four rotating barrels containing six darts each. When one barrel is empty, all you have to do is pull the second trigger to unleash the next load. The only trouble is, you might not get a chance to blast any zombies as they're sure to turn and run as soon as you show them this awesome machine!

ZOMBIE STRIKE
LOCKED AND LOADED

THE ZOMBIE INVASION HAD HIT US HARD.

I VOLUNTEERED TO TAKE ON THE NIGHT SHIFT AND HAD JUST SETTLED DOWN INTO MY BUNKER WHEN... THEY CAME.

ONE WAS ALREADY TRYING TO BREAK THROUGH MY DEFENCES. HE'D GRABBED A TELEVISION SET AND WAS ABOUT TO LAUNCH, PLUS THERE WERE COUNTLESS OTHERS BEHIND HIM – READY TO ATTACK.

LUCKILY, I'D BROUGHT MY OWN HEAVY DUTY WEAPON. THE SLEDGEFIRE. THE TV ADDICT TURNED AND RAN AS I BLASTED THREE DARTS HIS WAY AT ONCE.

SLEDGEFIRE

ALTHOUGH I'D SCARED THE FIRST ZOMBIE, PLENTY OF HIS FRIENDS WERE STILL ON THE ATTACK.

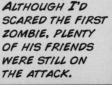

I DIDN'T PANIC, I KNEW I HAD STRENGTH ON MY SIDE.

SOON THE ZOMBIE CREW WERE GONE AND ALL WAS QUIET APART FROM THE DISTANT RUNNING FOOTSTEPS OF A SCARED ZOMBIE.

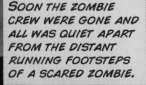

I KNEW THERE WAS STILL A LONG NIGHT AHEAD OF ME, BUT WITH THE SLEDGEFIRE AT MY SIDE, I WAS READY FOR ANYTHING.

ZOMBIE STRIKE
TV FANATIC

You think zombies are the bad guys? Think again. Being a zombie isn't all fun and games, for example, I haven't watched TV for weeks!

Carl Heckleman
Former Plumber
Now TV loving zombie

And then, I saw it. My old TV set! I'd just scooped it up when this kid jumped out of nowhere with a Sledgfire! I mean, talk about an overreaction!

So, the kid starts firing three darts at once at my fellow zombies and I have to make a choice, drop the TV or become dart-fodder. It was a no-brainer.

I tried to explain that all I wanted was to watch my cartoons, but I decided the only thing was to cut and run – and zombies don't run!

So, as much as I love TV – it just isn't worth the risk, when a kid with a blaster is standing between you and your favourite shows, it might be time to start thinking about another hobby...

Maybe I'll try knitting?

NERF

ZOMBIE STRIKE

WHAT TO DO

1. Cut around the dotted lines to make your mask. If you don't want to cut these pages out of your annual, copy the pages onto some thin card, instead.

2. Use a hole punch to make two holes in each of the masks.

36

Masks

Make these cool masks then turn to **Page 40** to play the Zombie Strike: Secret Zombie game!

3. Thread some elastic through the holes. Make a knot at each end to keep the elastic in place.

4. Slip on your mask, grab your blaster and get ready for the zombie invasion!

NERF

ZOMBIE STRIKE
STRIKESIDE SHOWDOWN

KEEPING YOUR ENERGY UP IS VITAL WHEN YOU'RE ON A MISSION. THAT'S WHY I WAS PATROLLING MAIN STREET ON THE HUNT FOR SUPPLIES. I WAS KEEPING MY EYES OPEN AND MY BLASTER CLOSE AT HAND.

SUDDENLY, THEY WERE ON ME. A GROUP OF THE UGLIEST ZOMBIES YOU COULD EVER WISH TO MEET. LUCKILY I HAD MY SLINGFIRE READY TO TAKE THEM OUT.

I WAS HANDLING THE SITUATION JUST FINE, UNTIL THE BIG ONE ROUNDED ON ME. IT WAS THEN THAT I REALISED I HAD RUN OUT OF DARTS. THINGS JUST GOT INTERESTING...

I TOSSED ASIDE MY SLINGFIRE AND REACHED FOR MY SIDESTRIKES, BUT BEFORE I HAD A CHANCE TO FIRE THE ZOMBIE'S ARMS FELL OFF! (AN OCCUPATIONAL HAZARD FOR THESE GUYS).

I DECIDED TO GIVE THE BIG GUY A FREE PASS, AND INSTEAD I FIRED THE DARTS AT HIS FEET TO WATCH HIM DANCE - HE WASN'T THAT BAD! THAT GUY HAD SOME MOVES, FOR AN UN-DEAD DUDE.

HE TOOK OFF WHILE HE HAD THE CHANCE, LEAVING ME AND MY SIDESTRIKES TO ONCE AGAIN PATROL MAIN STREET.

I KNEW IT WOULDN'T BE LONG BEFORE I'D HAVE TO DO BATTLE AGAIN...

HI! THE NAME'S BIG JIM AND THAT THERE IS MY BEST COW, BESSIE. SHE'S ALWAYS WANDERING OFF. THIS ONE TIME, SHE'D GONE AND GOT HERSELF LOST DOWN ON MAIN STREET...

SO I GOES TO LOOK FOR HER. I WASN'T HAVING MUCH LUCK, AND THAT'S WHEN I SAW THIS KID. HE LOOKED KINDA FRIENDLY SO I THOUGHT I'D GO AND SAY HI – SEE IF HE'D SEEN BESSIE.

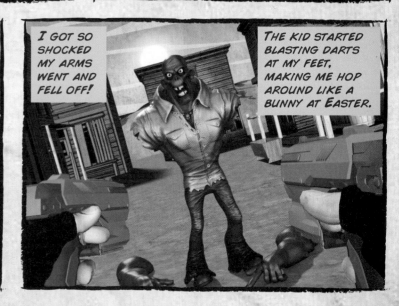

THE KID HAD THIS WEIRD LOOK ON HIS FACE, BUT HE WAS SMILING SO I THOUGHT HE MIGHT WANT TO HELP ME LOOK. IT WAS THEN HE PULLED OUT HIS BLASTERS!

I GOT SO SHOCKED MY ARMS WENT AND FELL OFF!

THE KID STARTED BLASTING DARTS AT MY FEET, MAKING ME HOP AROUND LIKE A BUNNY AT EASTER.

I DIDN'T WAIT AROUND TO SEE WHAT HE'D DO NEXT. I HID OUT ALL DAY UNTIL I COULD GO BACK WITH BESSIE AND GET MY ARMS BACK.

I LEARNED MY LESSON ALL RIGHT. YOU DON'T MESS WITH KIDS WITH BLASTERS... OR GET TOO CLOSE TO A CAMPFIRE!

NERF ZOMBIE STRIKE

SECRET ZOMBIE

Grab your masks, blasters and a bunch of mates to play this exciting game!

HOW TO PLAY:

1. Copy the names below onto scraps of paper, ball them up and put them in a bag or cup.

2. Pick out a character, then read up on your chosen mission. NOTE: If you are the Undercover Zombie, keep it quiet and pretend you are just part of the zombie clan.

3. The Zombie Strike Taskforce must choose a mascot to hide in their HQ. Your mascot must be defended from the zombies at all times!

4. Spread out in a park, garden or in a house. Then unleash the un-dead! The zombies must try and capture the mascot to take over HQ for their zombie clan!

YOU WILL NEED:

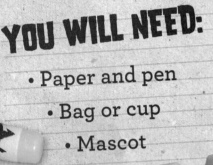

- Paper and pen
- Bag or cup
- Mascot

THE RULES:

- If a zombie touches you, you instantly become a zombie.
- If a zombie is hit by three darts, they are out of the game.

NAMES:

- Strike Leader x1
- Strike Sergeant x1
- Strike Taskforce (as many as needed)
- Chief Zombie x1
- Undercover Zombie x1
- Zombie (as many needed)

STRIKE LEADER

MISSION OBJECTIVE:

As head of the Zombie Strike Taskforce it's your job to eliminate all zombies in the area and defend your mascot in HQ. It's up to you to tell your taskforce where to station themselves during the operation, as well as being up front where all the action is taking place. Remember, if the zombies infiltrate HQ and steal the mascot, it'll be your neck on the line. Literally!

STRIKE SERGEANT

MISSION OBJECTIVE:

To support the Strike Leader at all times and, crucially, to take over command if your leader is turned into a zombie! Make sure your troops have enough darts to see them through the mission and cover your bravest task members as they do battle.

STRIKE TASKFORCE

MISSION OBJECTIVE:

To stop the zombies from taking the mascot in HQ (and not to get touched by a hungry zombie!) You'll need to listen to your team and be the bravest taskforce member out there.

CHIEF ZOMBIE

ZOMBIE MISSION:

To lead your rabble of un-dead delinquents to the Strike's HQ and retrieve their mascot. Then, and only then, will the zombies be free to roam the streets. Gather your zombies together to make a plan of action. Remember, zombies don't use blasters, so you'll need all those extra brains to get to the mascot un-detected.

CRAZY ZOMBIE

ZOMBIE MISSION:

To end years of Taskforce rule by taking the HQ mascot! As a zombie, all you need to do is touch a Taskforce member to turn them into a zombie, too. Listen to your chief, stick to the plan and the zombies will reign supreme!

UNDERCOVER ZOMBIE

ZOMBIE MISSION:

To stop the zombies from capturing the HQ mascot, without the zombies realising what you are up to! Keep your true allegiance a secret, but do everything you can to stop your zombie comrades from zombie-fying Taskforce members!

ZOMBIE STRIKE
SLINGFIRE STORM

WATCH THIS!

IT WAS RAINING HARD THAT NIGHT, SO I DECIDED TO TAKE A SHORTCUT BACK TO BASE. WHEN YOU'RE ON YOUR OWN, YOU NEED TO WATCH YOUR BACK AT ALL TIMES.

I HEARD A NOISE AND TURNED. WHEN I TURNED BACK AROUND HE WAS WAITING FOR ME. A ZOMBIE, ARMED AND READY TO STRIKE.

WITH ONE SWING OF MY BLASTER I WAS READY TO TAKE HIM ON. HE USED THE DUSTBIN LID AS A SHIELD AND MY DARTS COULDN'T GET THROUGH.

HE THREW THE METAL LID AT ME, HARD, BUT I CAUGHT IT JUST IN TIME. THE ZOMBIE KNEW HE WAS NO MATCH FOR THE SLINGFIRE AND TOOK HIS OPPORTUNITY TO RUN.

HE'D VANISHED INTO THE COLD, WET NIGHT LEAVING ME WITH MY TRUSTY BLASTER AND A NEW SHIELD TO ADD TO MY ARMOURY!

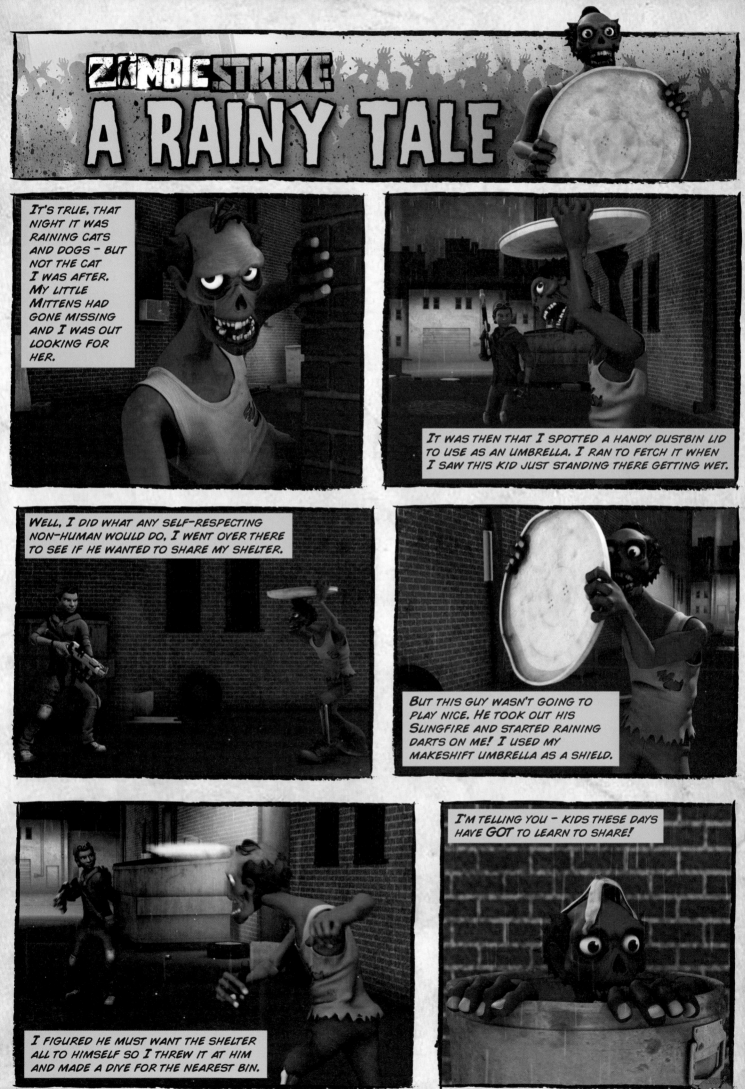

ZOMBIE SUDOKU

Complete the grid so that each image only appears once in each row, column and mini square.

WHERE'S YOUR... ULTIMATE BATTLEGROUND

Are you happiest wading through tropical swamps or scoping out the urban jungle? Find out!

QUESTION 1

Would you rather be...

A	Too hot
B	Too cold
C	Too wet
D	Too dry

QUESTION 2

Animals are...

A	Amazing. The more the better.
B	Great. But could get in the way.
C	Bad news. They distract you from your mission.
D	Dangerous. Probably.

QUESTION 3

What's your mission style?

A	I'm all action and ready for anything.
B	I plan carefully, but like extreme situations.
C	Laid back. I keep my eyes open and my blaster close.
D	I like to go solo.

QUESTION 4

What's your favourite style of blaster?

A	The bigger the better – with lots of darts!
B	Something trustworthy and lightweight.
C	A small, hand-held blaster I can hide in my coat.
D	A blaster with lots of different functions.

QUESTION 5

What's the best accessory?

A	A utility belt to hold my darts and modifications.
B	A big coat for warmth with lots of pockets for rations.
C	Dark glasses, so no one can spot your next target.
D	A water bottle – for energy!

QUESTION 6

Friends on your mission are...

A	Welcome. Sharing your adventures is great.
B	OK, as long as they stick to the plan.
C	All around you.
D	Nowhere to be seen.

MOSTLY As

JUNGLE WARFARE!

You're an adventurer who's ready for anything. The jungle would suit you as there's always loads to explore and discover, plus it's really exciting, too!

MOSTLY Bs

ARCTIC ADVENTURER

You like to take your missions to extremes. The harder, the better! Your dream destination would be the north pole – just watch out for those polar bears!

MOSTLY Cs

AWESOME URBANITE

The city is the place to be for you. You love being able to sneak undercover and blend in with your surroundings – ready for that next top secret mission.

MOSTLY Ds

DESERTED

Sweltering in a hot desert with no one around for miles sounds like your idea of fun. You and your blaster would make an excellent team as you cross the wide expanse.

N-STRIKE MEGA
CYCLONESHOCK
GO BIG AND BOLD WITH A COMPACT BLASTER!

MEGA

CYCLONESHOCK

NERF

THE LOW-DOWN:

The coolest thing about the Mega CycloneShock has to be the amazing super-sized darts! These big foam Whistler Darts make a screaming sound as they fly through the air. For high-performance, Mega-sized blasting, the Nerf Mega CycloneShock blaster is right on target!

IN TRAINING

Always use the correct darts for your blaster. Darts that are too small won't give you the fore power you need, while darts that are too big run the risk of getting stuck in the barrel.

LARGER
DARTS →

↗

WHIRLWIND
WORDS

How many times does the word
'CYCLONESHOCK' appear in
this cyclone?

CYCLONESHOCKCYCLONESHOCKCYCLONESHO
CYCLONESHOCKCYCLONESHOCKCYCLONESHOCKCYCLO
CKCYCLONESHOCKCYCLONESHOCKCYCLONESH
NESHOCKCYCLONESHOCKCYCLONESHOCKCYCLONESHO
CKCYCLONESHOCKCYCLONESHOCKCYCLONESH
CKCYCLONESHOCKCYCLONESHOCKCYCLONE
DCKCYCLONESHOCKCYCLONESHOCKCYCLO
SHOCKCYCLONESHOCKCYCLONESHOCKC
NESHOCKCYCLONESHOCKCYCLONESHOCKCYCLONES
YCLONESHOCKCYCLONESHOCKCYCLONESHO
HOCKCYCLONESHOCKCYCLONESHOCKCYCLONESH
CKCYCLONESHOCKCYCLONESHOCKCYCLONE
DCKCYCLONESHOCKCYCLONESHOCK
SHOCKCYCLONESHOCKC
CYCLONESHOCKC
YCLONESHOCK
CYCLONESHO
CKCYCLONE
SHOCKCYCL
ONESHO
CKCYCL
ONESHO
CKCYCL
LONES
HOC
K

49

N-STRIKE MEGA
ROTOFURY FOREVER!

BIG DARTS, BIG BARREL. IT'S FULL ON FURY!

MEGA

NERF

NERF KNOWS

The RotoFury has one of the longest ranges of all Nerf guns thanks to the awesome Mega Darts and power behind the blaster.

● ● ● ● ○

IN TRAINING

For the ultimate long-range shot, keep your blaster at least 1 metre off the ground.

THE LOW-DOWN:

Unleash the rapid-fire of the Mega RotoFury blaster! This long-range blaster can launch your darts up to 21 meters. Who will withstand your attack when you can fire up to 10 Mega Whistler Darts at your target without reloading? The cool Whistler Darts will scream through the air as you dominate the battlefield with the rapid-firing Mega RotoFury blaster!

● ● ● ● ○

FIND THE FURY

Your mission depends on having the biggest blaster around, so what happens when you lose your darts? Work your way through the maze to find your darts, load your Rotofury and defeat your enemies.

START

N-STRIKE MEGA
ROTOFURY RAMPAGE

CREATE AN ARENA AND TEST YOUR SPEED AND SKILL.

YOU WILL NEED

Five 'targets' – these could be toys, books, paper cups, cardboard boxes etc

Stopwatch

Blasters

HOW TO PLAY

ONE

Place targets around a garden, park or house if it's raining. This will be your arena.

TWO

Come up with an order to hit your targets and write it down.

TOP TIP!

Make sure you use a blaster with enough fire-power for all your targets. You don't want to waste time reloading mid-run!

THREE

Take it in turns to go run the arena, hitting the targets as you go. You can't move on to the next target until you've hit the previous one.

FOUR

Time each player's run around the arena. You have two attempts to get the best time! What are you waiting for?

MEGA SHOOTING RANGE

Make this cool range to challenge friends, or just keep your aim sharp!

HOW TO MAKE YOUR TARGETS:

1. Take your lollipop sticks and glue them together by overlapping the ends slightly. You'll want at least three different length sticks.

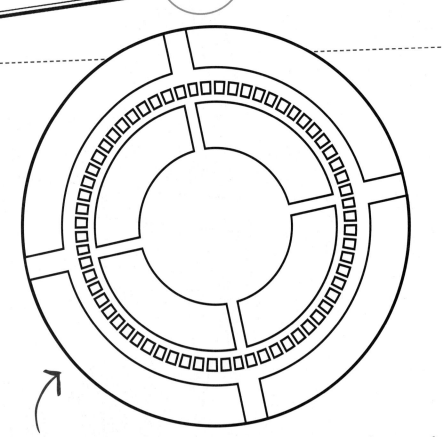

2. Glue the tip of your stick to a paper plate, then paint the whole thing black.

3. Trace the targets, above, onto paper, do this three times (or more if you want more targets). Colour them in then cut them out. Glue the targets onto each paper plate.

4. Tie a length of string 10 cm long to the end of each target.

HOW TO MAKE YOUR RANGE:

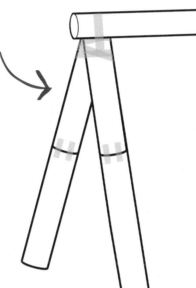

1. Make a 2cm slit in the end of one of your kitchen roll tubes, overlap the flaps slightly and insert into another tube to make a long pole. Add a piece of sticky tape to secure.

2. Repeat step one to make three more poles.

3. Make a final, longer pole with your three remaining tubes using the same technique.

4. Take two of the shorter tubes and tape the ends together to make an upside down V shape. Use plenty of tape to make sure it's secure. Repeat with the remaining shorter poles.

5. Place the longer pole between the two V shapes. This will form the crossbar of your shooting range. Tape in place.

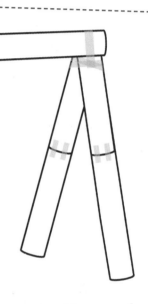

6. Paint your structure and leave to dry.

HOW TO PLAY:

Tie your targets to the crossbar of your shooting range. Take up a position and start blasting!

DO YOU KNOW YOUR...

BLASTERS?

Have you got in-depth Nerf knowledge? Let's find out!

Check your answers on page 60

QUESTION 1
What two items come with the Modulus Strike & Defend upgrade kit?

1. ....
2. ....

QUESTION 2
Apart from their size, what's so special about the Mega Darts?

....

QUESTION 3
Which blaster is this?

....

QUESTION 4
How many darts can the Flipfury hold?

....

IT'S NERF OR NOTHIN'!

QUESTION 5

What are the three main colours of the Doominator?

1. ....
2. ....
3. ....

QUESTION 6

How many different types of dart are there?

....

QUESTION 7

Which one of these is NOT a real Zombie?

Big Jim Doolin

Billy 'Brains' McGovern

Carl Heckleman

....

QUESTION 8

How far can the CycloneShock blaster fire?

'MEGA

CYCLONESHOCK

NERF

....

QUESTION 9

What is the Red Dot Sight accessory for the Modulus Blaster's main function?

NERF

....

QUESTION 10

How many darts does the flip clip hold?

....

BRAIN TRAINING

Being on top of your game isn't all about your skill with a blaster, you've got to keep your mind sharp, too! See if you can complete these awesome puzzles.

UNDERCOVER BLASTERS

Name these undercover blasters!

1

2

3

1. ....

2. ....

3. ....

FITFURY WORDS

Can you fit all the words into the grid? We've done the first one for you.

BLASTER
MODULUS
STRIKE
DART
ZOMBIE
MEGA
ELITE

DART-RITHMATICS

How many darts do you need to win these challenges?

1 Three Zombies are approaching, each of them has brought a friend for company. It takes two darts to destroy each zombie.

2 Your battle ground has five targets which must be hit 7 times.

3 You've got three friends in your battle group and 16 darts. How many darts do you each get?

MEMORY MEN

Can you remember what blasters these Zombie fighters used?

1. _____

2. _____

3. _____

MODULUS MAKE UP

Which three parts of the Modulus are missing?

1. _____

2. _____

3. _____

ANSWERS

PAGE 7: LABEL IT

1. Dual Rail Barrel
2. Darts
3. Motorized Blaster
4. Targeting Scope
5. Drop Grip
6. Banana Grip
7. Storage Stock

PAGE 11: COVERT OPERATIONS

Bring more darts

PAGE 25: VISION VERIFICATION

PAGE 22: SEEK & DESTROY

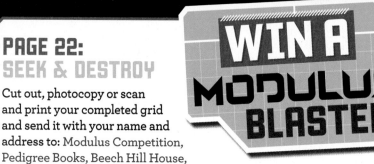

Cut out, photocopy or scan and print your completed grid and send it with your name and address to: Modulus Competition, Pedigree Books, Beech Hill House, Walnut Gardens, Exeter, Devon EX4 4DH

Entires must be received by 29th January 2016.

All vaild* entries will be checked by Pedigree Books Ltd. Winners will be notified by 12th February 2016 and prizes sent out within 30 days.

WIN A MODULUS BLASTER

PAGE 44: ZOMBIE SUDOKU

PAGE 49: WHIRLWIND WORDS

'CycloneShock' appears 44 times in the cyclone!

PAGE 51: FIND THE FURY

PAGES 56-57:
DO YOU KNOW YOUR BLASTERS?

1. Blaster stock and Blast shield
2. They whistle through the air
3. The CrossBolt
4. 12
5. Green, red and grey
6. 10
7. Billy 'Brains' McGovern
8. Up to 21 meters
9. To give you precision aim
10. 24

PAGES 58-59:
BRAIN TRAINING

UNDERCOVER BLASTERS

1. Modulus
2. The CrossBolt
3. Flipfury

FITFURY WORDS

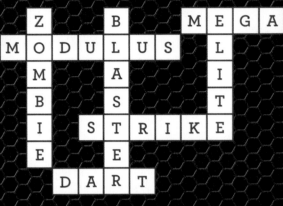

DART-RITHMATICS

1. 12   2. 35   3. 4

MEMORY MEN

1. Sledgefire

2. Sidestrikes

3. Slingfire

MODULUS MAKE UP

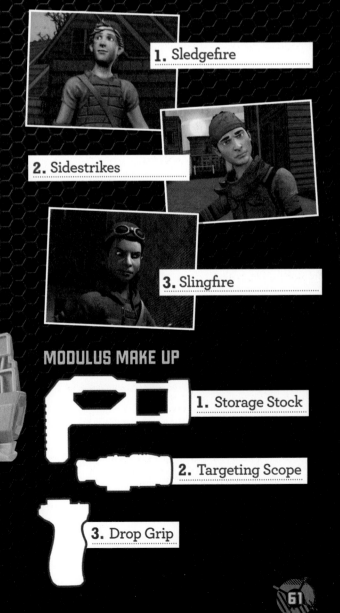

1. Storage Stock

2. Targeting Scope

3. Drop Grip

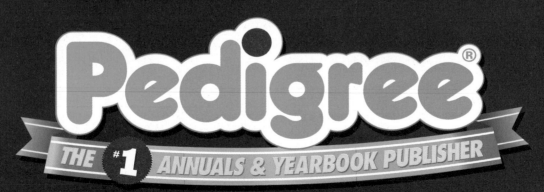